Mission Tales

Volume 1

The Miracle Ship (*Mission San Diego*)

A tale of the beginning of the famous California Missions and the first critical year at San Diego.

Father Peyri's Shadows (*Mission San Luis Rey*)

ts.

Capistrano)

g super-

Gabriel)

arned to

lo Rey)

ra.

dener.

f exile on a lonely

Inés)

he Mission.

youth, his grand-

The Tilemaker (*Mission San Luis Obispo*)

A story about a young Indian's part in the perfecting of tiles.

Mission Tales

By HELEN M. ROBERTS
Illustrated by Muriel Lawrence

Volume 3

The Lone Woman of San Nicolas
A Tale of Mission Santa Barbara
Page 3

Pasquala of Santa Ines
A Tale of Mission Santa Inés
Page 35

The Anger of Chupu
A Tale of Mission Purisima
Page 65

PACIFIC BOOKS, PUBLISHERS
PALO ALTO, CALIFORNIA

T 1599

The Lone Woman of San Nicolas

Mission Santa Barbara

INTRODUCTION

THIS is the story of a lone Indian woman who was marooned on a bleak island in the Santa Barbara Channel. She was rescued after many years, and when she at last reached Mission Santa Barbara she found both joy and sorrow within its shelter.

Mission Santa Barbara was founded nearly seventy years earlier. From the gentle slopes of the Santa Inés Mountains, this tenth Mission, the "Queen of the Missions," overlooks the ocean and the distant islands of the Santa Barbara Channel.

Very soon after its founding, Chumash Indians came to the Mission in large numbers. Under the padres' skillful training they learned to build their own adobe houses, which they whitewashed neatly inside and out. Their Indian village was arranged around a large plaza, where the children and young people learned to garden. The older Indians, too, learned many valuable skills—carpentering, tanning, weaving, sewing, gardening, and cattle raising. Altogether, six hundred Chumash Indians worked faithfully under the guidance of the padres.

5

Building activity at Mission Santa Barbara was a continuous process. New and larger structures were built to replace the earlier ones. After Captain Vancouver visited the Mission in 1793, he wrote in his book that he considered Santa Barbara the best-constructed and the best-kept of all the Missions he had seen. At a still later period, the fourth church was constructed. This is the church which is widely known and admired today. Its six-foot-thick sandstone walls are crowned with two massive bell towers. The beauty and grandeur of this Mission building have influenced architecture even beyond the borders of California.

Still other structures at Mission Santa Barbara have endured for more than a century. A large reservoir which collected water from the hills is still in use. The beautiful fountain where Juana looked at her reflection continues to flow today. But standing empty and unused is the long basin where the Indian women formerly washed their clothes and rinsed them in fresh water spouting from a cement bear's head.

Mission Santa Barbara had its difficult period too. When news came that the pirate Bouchard was within a few miles of this Mission, soldiers and Indians prepared to defend it, but he did not attack.

A few years later, enemy Indians attacked it in force. Fires swept over the hills, burned the trees, threatened the Mission, and blackened its vineyards. At another time there was a drought so serious that the people marched through the streets and prayed for rain.

One of the greatest blows to Mission Santa Barbara, as well as to the other Missions, was the decree of secularization. About ten years after Mexico became an independent nation, the new government decided on a plan which would remove the California Missions from the control of the Church. The first step was to "free" the Indians from the padres' rule. But when few Indians seemed eager for this "freedom," another step was taken. Only Indians who were free would be allowed to vote in their village election. Because most of the Indians were devoted to the padres, even this decree had little effect.

In the following year, 1834, the actual decree of secularization was passed. This act provided that the Indians and the Mission property were to be removed from the control of the Franciscan padres. Administrators, or "secular" officials, were then to govern both the Missions and the Indians. Inventories were taken at all the Missions, and the new officials in charge received salaries which were paid out of the Missions' earnings. Mexican padres were to replace the Spanish Franciscans. Under this secular control, both the padres and the poor Mission Indians suffered. Mission buildings and ranches were sadly neglected, and Mission prosperity gradually came to an end.

During this difficult period, however, a new padre came to Mission Santa Barbara in the company of Bishop Diego, California's first bishop. This young Mexican priest, Father Francisco Sánchez, was a man of unusual zeal and devotion. For forty-two years he worked among California's Indians and Mexicans. Today he is probably better known to readers of *Ramona* as Father Salvierderra, a man beloved by all. In 1853, when the Lone Woman of San Nicolas reached Mission Santa Barbara, it was this same understanding Father Sánchez who welcomed her and later baptized her at the Mission which had sheltered many of her people.

MISSION SANTA BARBARA

CALENDAR

1786 Founding of the Mission, December 4
1820 Dedication of the present church
1834 Secularization
1842 Arrival of Father Sánchez
1846 Sale of the Mission
1865 Return of the Mission to the Catholic Church

THE LONE WOMAN OF SAN NICOLAS

THE cold gray fog settled down over the rocky island of San Nicolas, farthest westward of the Santa Barbara Channel Islands. Gelma stood on the beach and shivered. Even her cloak of smooth sea-otter skin could not shut out the cold and dampness of such a day. She stared at the cliff where breakers were dashing high above the jagged rocks, adding their constant pounding roar to the screeching of sea gulls.

"If only the sun would shine!" Gelma said to her sister. "When I see nothing but fog day after day, I am restless and unhappy."

The older Indian woman touched Gelma's arm and pointed seaward. "Look!" she urged. "The fog is drifting now. Maybe it will blow away and you can have your sunshine. All of us will be happier if the sun shines."

Gelma noticed a tiny patch of water where blue waves danced and sparkled in a shaft of light. Suddenly the patch widened, showing the sunlight which soon flooded the island with its warmth.

And offshore, tossing about on the choppy waves, was a small boat.

"A boat! A boat!" shouted Gelma.

Indians hurried out of their huts to see the welcome sight. Gelma darted into her hut and carried her small boy to the shore to watch the arrival of the rowboat. As it came closer she could see several people. Indians were rowing the boat, but three white men were in it too.

"Those are not Russians," said Gelma, surprised.

"They are strangers," agreed her sister. "Russian fur traders said they would never come here again. But perhaps these palefaces are traders too."

Gelma watched the village children shouting and laughing as they ran along the narrow strip of sandy beach. Even one day of sunshine brought joy to young and old alike. And now, visitors! She put her small son down on the beach and wished for his sake that all the days could be warm and bright like this one.

As the rowboat nosed up on the beach, Indians crowded around it. Children tumbled into it and climbed out again, carrying strange fruits in their brown hands. One of the Indians who had come in the boat spoke for the white men in a language that the islanders could partly understand.

"We come from Missions on mainland," he said slowly.

At first Gelma did not pay much attention to his words. She did not understand "Missions." She was far more interested in the bright clothes the Indians were wearing. Gaily striped blankets were wrapped around their shoulders covering most of their clothes except the blue-gray trousers. It was not until the strange Indians offered fruit to the islanders that Gelma became really interested in their explanations.

"At Missions we grow beautiful fruit—apples, peaches, plums, pears, and oranges." The man's words were not so interesting as the sweet fruit he offered. Except for an occasional wild berry, this fruit was the first that Gelma had ever tasted. She ate one piece hungrily, then reached for another to give to her little boy.

"What are these Missions?" asked the chief of the island. "Tell us more!"

The visiting Indian looked around him and pointed to the barren island where few trees grew and where huts were made of whale skeletons covered with furs. "At Missions are warm huts, comfortable beds, plenty of food three times a day."

Gelma sighed. Was it possible that any place

had such good things? "Does sun shine at Missions?" she asked, trembling at her own boldness.

The strange Indian nodded and smiled. "Sun all year long," he promised. "Wonderful church and gray-robed padres. Beautiful music!"

Gelma shook her head, not understanding about the church and the padres. She wondered about the music too. There was little music on San Nicolas Island, and that little was mournful and shrill. But at that moment one of the Indians and the white men began to sing a joyous song. The other Indian took something shiny from the bottom of the boat, held it to his lips, and played sweet music that made the islanders long to dance.

Gelma needed nothing more to persuade her to go away to the mainland, but it was not her place to speak. She had nothing to say about what her people would do. The Mission song ended far too soon to suit her. Then the island chief spoke simply. "Do Indians live at this Mission?"

The first Mission Indian answered, "Hundreds of Indians live there! Padres sent us here to ask you to come and join us."

"We play much but we work too," the other added eagerly.

The Chief called the men of the village into his

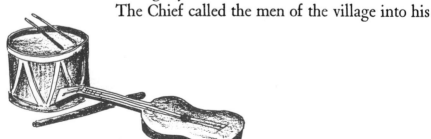

hut for a council meeting. Gelma listened anxiously to the voices which were louder than usual. She smiled when the Chief announced solemnly, "We go to Mission."

All the islanders began to crowd closer to the boat until the Mission Indians waved them back. "Wait!" they shouted. "We must return to our ship, which is anchored offshore. Then we can bring another rowboat. We have room for only a few this time. While we are gone, get ready everything you wish to take with you!" But the Indians refused to go until they could all leave their island at once.

After the boat had disappeared into the fog, the Chief called his people together for a few minutes. "Pack only what you really need!" he ordered. "But leave nothing of value behind you for Russian fur traders to steal."

Gelma took her little boy, hurried to her sister's hut, and began sorting furs and baskets of food. "Always sunshine," she murmured. "Warm days, good food, and wonderful music." She was so happy that she tried to sing the chant the strangers had sung.

"Why, Gelma!" her sister said. "You are singing for the first time in many years."

Gelma's eyes grew bright. "I am happy for all of us, but mostly for the little one."

The older woman sorted her few belongings while her children danced in and out of the hut. Never before had there been such great excitement on San Nicolas Island. At last one of the children shouted shrilly, "The boats are coming!"

The villagers hurried to the beach to watch. When the boats were close to the shore, the Chief gave final orders to his people. "Bring all your supplies to the beach! And toss the fur coverings from your huts into the sea."

Now that the Indians were ready to leave the only home they had ever known, they were silent— all but Gelma, who felt nothing but joy over leaving the dismal island. "Take this pile of furs for my baby," she said to her sister's oldest child.

"No!" cried the girl. "I'll take care of your little boy!"

At that moment the boats reached shore. "Hurry!" cried the Mission Indians. "A storm is coming! No time to lose! We'll help you!"

The soldiers showed the Indians where to sit in the bottom of the boat. They pushed women and frightened children into their places. Suddenly Gelma remembered the good furs still covering the

whale-bone hut. She and her sister were both widows with no man to help them. She ran back to the hut. In a moment she had stripped off the furs and tossed them into the sea. She was glad to see the breakers snatch them away where no trader would get them. By the time she returned to the beach, the first boat had pushed away from shore. As she stopped to pick up her supplies, impatient hands pushed her into the other boat.

Separated now from her sister's family and her child, Gelma was frightened among so many strangers. The waves through which they were rowing grew higher with every passing moment. The fog banks were shifting across the blue-gray water and shutting out both the other boat and the island from sight.

With one hand Gelma clung tightly to her package of furs, and with the other she gripped the edge of the boat. To calm her fears she thought of the perfect days ahead when she and her son would enjoy the warm sunshine and the fine Mission food.

At last the rowboat drew close to the large, winged ship. Gelma was the first to climb on board and hurry to the wide deck. Standing beside the captain she watched for the other boat to appear out of the fog. Even before she caught a glimpse of it, she heard screams she recognized. Then she saw the crowded boat and her sister trying to quiet the screams of the little girl. But where was Gelma's small boy? What had happened to her child?

Gelma's heart was like lead. She shouted to her sister, but the little girl's screams drowned out her words. She shook the captain's arm. "Send a boat back! My baby has been left behind!" But the captain only shook his head.

Panic gripped the young mother. There was no time to lose. If she waited, someone might stop her. She could not forsake her child. She ran to the other side of the ship, tore off her fur cloak and leaped into the water.

Gelma was a strong young woman, toughened by years of struggle against nature. She swam easily enough for a short distance. But never before had she tried a long swim against mountainous waves and opposing tides. At first she swam breathlessly in a hurry to reach shore. But soon her breath came in gasps that forced her to rest. On and on she swam, steadily, wearily, carried off her course time after time.

Often the island was swallowed up in a fog bank, but she could tell the right direction by the booming of the breakers against the cliffs. At last a long,

sweeping breaker lifted her and swept her high up on the shallow beach. There she lay, too beaten and bruised to be able to move for a long time.

Staggering, stumbling, she found her way to her hut. But she found no sign of her child. Blankets, food, and baby were gone! She dragged herself out into the bitter cold evening. She called frantically for her child. Then she crept back inside the shelter and sank down in a heap.

All that night Gelma lay in a stupor. In the morning a streak of sunshine came through the fog and wakened her. She listened a moment for the sound of her baby's breathing, but she heard only the beating of her heart. All at once she clearly realized the dreadful truth. She was alone, alone on San Nicolas Island, miles and miles away from her people.

Her grief, loneliness, and despair drove her screaming out of the hut. She raced up the rocky shore to a cliff. But there were only the sea gulls to scream back at her. Fog surrounded her island like walls. She knew now that she was completely forsaken and that she should not expect anyone to come back for her.

Her screaming ceased. She was hungry and cold. She wandered from hut to hut. They were all de-

serted and empty. She could not find even a blanket or scrap of fur. There was no fire remaining in any of the huts. Because of a shortage of wood, the island houses had been made of parts of whale skeletons covered over with furs. But the furs were gone now, and the white bones of the wide open mouths were all that remained of the village. She pried some mussels away from rocks at the water's edge, scooped them out of their shells, and gulped them down raw.

"I must make fire to keep myself alive," she thought. "Without fire or clothing I will soon perish."

Patiently she gathered dried grasses and leaves. In the shelter of her whale-skull hut she ground them to a powder. For hours she twirled a stick around in a small hole, faster and faster, never giving up until a few sparks set fire to the powdery grass. She sighed a long, weary sigh. "Never can I let my fire go out," she muttered to herself. "Now there is no one to help me. I must learn to depend upon myself and I must keep myself strong. Some day I may be rescued!"

Fortunately, that evening Gelma found a worn sea-otter skin, full of small holes which she patched from scraps cut from the ragged edges. It would

last her a long time if she wore it only in the coldest weather.

When roots and shellfish became scarce on the island, Gelma thought of the foods at the Mission— the juicy peaches, pears, and plums she had sampled. Sometimes in her dreams she was surrounded with mounds of food and her old friends, who were watching her eat it. Then her waking was still harder to bear.

When Gelma began to feel the cold wintry fogs, she wove grasses into a kind of skirt. But when the wind roared across the island or the wet fog settled on it for days and weeks, there was not nearly enough warmth in her grass skirt and the worn skin cloak.

The desolate Indian woman searched the island for any supplies that might have been left behind. She found a few flint knives and used them in making bone fishhooks and needles, and for digging roots. Every day she climbed up to the lookout rock, always with a faint hope that a ship might return for her.

Once when Gelma sighted a whale stranded in the shallow water, she shouted for the first time in many moons. She recalled those gay days long ago when all the islanders had cut and dried enough

whale meat for the entire season. But with one knife and one pair of hands, only a small amount of meat could be cut. After a few days the odor of the rapidly spoiling meat along the shore sickened Gelma until she could scarcely eat. But her hunger drove her on. She had to eat.

Years dragged by. There was little difference between the seasons on her bleak island. Rain in winter, fog in summer, and only an occasional sunny day! Gelma could tell the passing of the years by the shortening of the days, when it grew dark earlier than usual. On what seemed the shortest day she made a deep notch in the whale bone at the right of her doorway.

One day in spring she heard a new sound and found a drift log bumping against the jagged rocks beyond the cliff. Quickly she swam out to it and tugged with all her strength to free it. After many hours she freed it from the rocks and pushed it before her to the shore, where she pulled it up on the beach to dry.

"A dugout canoe," she murmured to herself. "With it I can paddle to the nearest island. Or when the wind is right I can drift to the mainland." In her thoughts she always added "to my baby." But then she quickly turned her thoughts to something else

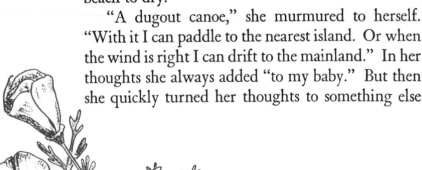

because she could never be sure whether her child had been sleeping safely in the bottom of the boat or whether— She dared not think about that. She had to keep busy.

She spent many long hours digging into the log with her flint knives. It might take a lifetime to hollow out a canoe. Her knives might not last until she had finished it. When she had cut a small hole she laid a fire in it to burn it out. But the log had been soaked with water, and it showed little sign of drying. The dismal fogs kept it too damp to burn. Her fire kept smouldering, and then she would have to relight it.

As the years dragged by, Gelma cut notches in the log as well as in the whale bone to mark the passage of time. Even with these two records she became uncertain about the exact number of years. She shrugged her bony shoulders. "What difference does the time make?" she thought. "It may be five years or ten. Or it may be all my life."

Yet each spring with the coming of the new green leaves on the scrubby bushes and with the coming of the green grasses and occasional wild flowers, she again felt new hope. She noticed the large flocks of birds that stopped at her island— birds on their way to better climates. She could not

fly away with them as she wished, but she could at least use them for food.

Gelma built little bird traps of twigs and grasses. When she found how easily she could catch birds in them, she built many more traps and scattered them over the island. She needed the food desperately. Then after a while she began to think of all the little skins. What a beautiful dress they would make! Unlike anything ever seen before. Of course there would be no one to see her dress, but she would find joy in it, and besides, the feathers would help keep her warm.

Very carefully she saved every bird skin, tiny or large. She rubbed them with seaweed and dried them tenderly to preserve the pretty feathers. In the long, dreary evenings beside her fire, she sewed these skins together with a fishbone needle and with thread made of fiber. The colors pleased the lonely woman. Yet always she kept whispering, "Mission clothes! Mission clothes!" and then, "Mission food!" until the words formed a sort of chant while she sewed.

With every passing year there were more gashes on her log and her whale bone. There were more than she could count on all her fingers. Yet no ship had come for her! Sometimes, watching from her

lookout on a clear day, she would think she saw a
sail; but, before she could be sure of it, a fog bank
would blot it from sight. Sometimes she thought
she saw people landing on her beach, but always it
was just a dream, a dreadfully disappointing dream.

It had been years now since Gelma had spoken
aloud. What use was speech when there was no one
to hear her? She thought a great deal and sometimes even moved her mouth in silent words. But
only the screaming sea gulls, the barking sea lions,
and the constantly pounding waves kept her company.

For a short time after her return to the island she
had thrown fish to the sea lions, hoping to coax them
to come close enough to be her friends. Then for a
while she had scarcely enough food for herself. At
last she decided it was better for the herds of sea
lions to catch their own fish, as long as she had to
eat whatever she could find and whenever she had
the chance. Unlike all other creatures she could not
leave the island!

At last she finished the bird-skin dress and
sewed it up over her body. A wild sense of freedom
came over her the moment she wore it. She knew
that the dugout canoe was little more than half done
and that she could not hope to get away from the

island. But she could leap from rock to rock and spread her feather-covered arms like wings in her wild dance. From one end of the island to the other she sped, almost like a great bird ready to sail away into the sky. She laughed and shouted wildly at the sea gulls, which screamed back at her and flew away as if mocking her helplessness.

Her shouting and laughter grew louder as she raced back toward her hut. Even when she saw white men and Indians she paid no attention. They must be another of her many dreams. This time she would not think about them. But when they spoke in a strange tongue she realized it was no dream.

"Come! Come back to the mainland with us!" they cried. They made their meaning clear by using signs. They tried to tell her that from their whaling ship they had seen the movement of the bright colors as she danced, and they had come to rescue her.

Gelma was afraid. She was terrified and happy at the same time. She ate the food they offered her; then she climbed silently into the boat, still dazed by the thought of their sudden appearance after eighteen long years of waiting. As they rowed out to the whaling ship, Gelma would not look back at her island prison. Never again did she want to see its

cold forbidding shores! On board the ship she ate all the fruit and bread the palefaces offered her. She held out her hand for more. After eighteen years of near-starvation, would she ever have enough food again? She kept shaking her head to make sure it was not a dream. Then she gripped the railing of the ship and knew she was not dreaming.

Closer to the mainland the fog cleared away. Suddenly the sun shone on a small city of dazzling white houses roofed with red tiles. It shone still brighter on a beautiful building farther up the hill. All of this was much grander than any of Gelma's dreams. Could this be the wonderful Mission she had longed for all these years? After hoping in vain, were her dreams really coming true?

Anxiously she watched the shore, longing for a glimpse of her people, who would be waiting to welcome her. Her heart pounded wildly. Where were all the Indians? She could not see an Indian anywhere.

When the rowboat at last reached shore, Mrs. Nidever, the wife of the ship's captain, opened her arms and held the forlorn woman tightly. But Gelma was dazed and bewildered. Her eyes kept searching for others, for her own dark-skinned people, to welcome her. Gray-robed Father Sánchez

greeted her with a friendly smile and led both the women into the shelter and quiet of the deserted Mission. But Gelma was frightened even more when she saw the strange candlelight flickering on the altar.

"Where are my people?" Gelma kept asking, over and over again. She repeated her words in a dreadful, wailing chant. But it was many weeks before she had learned enough of her friend's Spanish to understand about the fate of the Indians. When new rulers had given the Indians their freedom, they had left the Mission. Some of them were working on neighboring ranchos and some had disappeared completely. Gelma's heart felt numb. Then her loneliness returned, more dreadful than before.

Gelma asked the same pitiful questions of every visitor to the Mission. "Where are my people? Where are the Indians from San Nicolas Island?"

Kindly Father Sánchez showed her all the orchards that the Indians had planted. Perhaps her people had helped to build the sparkling fountain and the laundering trough. They might have helped decorate the wonderful white church. But where were they now? Were some of them in those unmarked graves in the Mission churchyard?

Gelma shook her head sadly. "Let me become

a Mission Indian too. Let me do what I can to help the Mission that once gave shelter to many of my people."

So the padre spent many hours with her, teaching her about the Mission God. Sometimes Gelma knelt alone on the smooth tiles inside the church. Sometimes she lighted an altar candle and prayed in her native tongue. "Let me see just one of my people! Just one!" she would repeat again and again.

Days were passing much more swiftly than they had seemed to pass on the island of San Nicolas. In just two weeks Gelma would be baptized in the wonderful Mission church. Often she wandered forlornly up into the hills beyond Santa Barbara. She kept hoping to meet some of her island people. Sometimes she wondered whether she would recognize them after so many years.

Meanwhile all the people in the village were very kind to her. They gave her more rich food than she could possibly eat. They were planning a big fiesta for the day when she would be baptized Juana María. In return for their kindness, Gelma had promised to dance a new bird dance in the same costume she had been wearing when she came to Santa Barbara.

30

One morning she was practicing her new dance, skipping, leaping, gliding across the balcony of the Nidever house. She could not keep her thoughts on her dance; she kept thinking, instead, of all her people. As she danced close to the railing, she glanced down into the street below. Suddenly she stood still and clung tightly to one of the posts. She stared at a young Indian, dressed in Mission clothes, who was walking past the house.

"Stop! Stop!" she shouted in her native tongue.

The young man looked up at her and shook his head. Then he replied in smooth-flowing Spanish that Gelma could not follow. But there was something in his fine, earnest young face that reminded Gelma of her people. As he walked away from her across the field toward the Mission he seemed even more familiar to her. She watched him until at last he disappeared down the long, arched corridors.

The lonely Indian woman stood on the balcony, lost in her memories. Could it be that her dreams, her new prayers, were about to come true?

"Gelma! Gelma!" It was Mrs. Nidever calling her. "Come, Gelma! Your lunch is waiting for you!"

Gelma looked at her friend a moment and sighed. "I can't eat," she said in halting Spanish.

"I must go to the Mission." In a mixture of her two languages she tried to tell Mrs. Nidever about the young Indian who had just walked by and gone to the Mission. "He looks like my people! He looks like my . . . ."

Mrs. Nidever put her arm around the trembling Indian woman. "We can ask Father Sánchez," she said. "He will surely know who the young man is."

Gelma's dark eyes glowed. "Could—could I have a new dress to wear?" she asked wistfully. "A Mission dress or else a Spanish dress?"

Mrs. Nidever showed her an old sea chest, filled with treasures from all parts of the world. "Which would you like to wear, Gelma?" she asked gently. "You may make your choice."

Admiringly, Gelma chose a long, rustling black dress and a gay embroidered shawl. She longed for beautifully embroidered satin slippers, too, but there were none to fit her feet. "We can make new slippers for you in time for the fiesta," promised Mrs. Nidever. "Now you are dressed just like a Spanish señora!"

The two women walked across the fields. Gelma lingered a moment to admire her reflection in the beautifully clear water of the fountain. Then she hurried over to the Mission church where Father

Sánchez was standing. She waited for Mrs. Nidever to speak.

"Good evening, Padre! Gelma wants to know if you can tell us about a certain young Indian who passed by our house a short time ago," explained Mrs. Nidever.

Father Sánchez looked at Gelma's fine new clothing and smiled at her. "Oh, yes! The boy has come from San Gabriel Mission," he answered in a friendly manner. "His name is Juan, almost the same as Juana, which will be your own name after your baptism. He is an orphan, about twenty years old, and he has come to look after our beautiful gardens, that have been long neglected. He is a fine boy! He has a good voice, too, and will be a great help in our choir. And he has strong and willing hands to devote to his Mission."

Gelma smiled and raised her head proudly. She lifted her rustling skirts a little, the way Spanish ladies did, and tiptoed down the aisle toward the front of the church. Then she knelt on the cool tile floor, bowed her head, and clasped her hands very tightly.

She couldn't be absolutely sure that Juan was one of her San Nicolas people. But in her heart she was sure that he was really her own son. They

would both be Mission Indians and do whatever they could to help the good padre.

At first Gelma prayed slowly, falteringly. Then her words burst forth in torrents of thanks which helped to wash from her memory all the old sorrow of her lonely years. New hope and a new-found happiness were being born within her.

Pasquala of Santa Inés

Mission Santa Inés

INTRODUCTION

PASQUALA was an Indian girl from the country of the Tulares in the San Joaquin Valley. Because her life had been saved by Father Uría of Mission Santa Inés, she longed to show her appreciation by doing something special for the Mission. The story of her hardships and of her heroism is told in "Pasquala of Santa Inés."

Mission Santa Inés was the nineteenth of the California Missions and the first one to be founded in the nineteenth century. It is located in the sheltered Santa Inés Valley in Santa Barbara County between San Luis Obispo and Santa Barbara. In its early years a number of the Indians trained at Mission Santa Barbara came to join the new Mission, and they brought others of their Chumash people with them. Within a few years the padres and the Indians had completed the quadrangle with its long church, dwellings, shops, and granary, all connected by tiled corridors.

In 1808 Father Uría came to Santa Inés and remained there for sixteen years. From the beginning he was interested in his Indians and in the welfare of the Mission. He brought into the Mission many of the Tulare Indians from the valley to the east of the mountains. As a people, the Tulares were fierce and unfriendly toward the Missions, and they were usually resentful when any of their villagers became Mission Indians. At one time a total of seven hundred Indians lived at Santa Inés in its compact village of dazzling white adobe huts.

Under Father Uría's supervision, the ranches and gardens flourished. The padres directed the building of an irrigation system, which brought water from the mountains to the orchards and vineyards. After the earthquake of 1812 a new church was built and decorated vividly by the Indians. At the height of prosperity came a well-planned attack by the Tulare Indians. This attack, which spread to several neighboring Missions, played an important part in this true story, "Pasquala of Santa Inés."

At Santa Inés and at all the other Missions, fiestas such as the one described in this story took place frequently. On the patron saint's day, on regular festival days, and on other special occasions at the Mission, Indians had a chance to celebrate. After the church service, they spent the remainder of the day in gay and exciting events. By this time the Indians

had become expert riders, and they enjoyed horse racing or any sport which featured horses. Sometimes visitors came from neighboring ranchos or Missions to take part in the sports. The cock chase gave them an opportunity to show their skill in horsemanship. In this "sport" they tied a rooster securely and buried him up to his neck. Riders rode full speed and snatched at the head as they passed it. "Tailing the bull" also required great skill in riding.

The bull-and-bear fight, though cruel, was always popular. After Indians had lassoed a bear in the mountains they brought it down to the Plaza and secured it by its hind legs. They next brought a bull close to the bear, and if the two animals did not fight immediately, the Indians prodded them until the struggle started. Usually the bull was the victor, but sometimes both animals were killed.

Dancing followed the other events. Sometimes Indians, painted in weird colors, performed their primitive dances.

After the Indian attack and revolt, Father Uría left Mission Santa Inés. For a time the Mission produced great amounts of grain, livestock, tallow, and wool. But with the coming of secularization the Indians lost interest and neglected the ranches. At

Santa Inés, in 1844, Bishop Diego established a school for boys, which continued for many years.

Early in this century Father Buckler came to the Mission. With the help of Fernando, an old Mission Indian, he repaired the Mission and brought order to it. Today its museum displays old music manuscripts and musical instruments once played by the Indians. Both a statue and a painting of Santa Inés remain in the Mission. In the graveyard are many unmarked Indian graves.

But young Pasquala needs no headstone to mark her resting place. Beautiful Mission Santa Inés is a symbol of the devotion of the padres and a memorial to the courageous Indian girl who risked her life for her Mission.

1804 Founding of the Mission, September 17
1808 Arrival of Father Uría
1817 Dedication of the present church
1824 Tulare Indian attack on the Mission
1836 Secularization
1846 Sale of the Mission
1862 Return of the Mission to the Catholic Church
1904 Coming of Father Buckler

PASQUALA OF SANTA INÉS

ASQUALA was the happiest Indian girl in all Santa Inés Mission. She lived with her mother and father in one of the new adobe houses, which were whitewashed both inside and out to keep them clean and fresh. But it was not the fine house that made her so happy. Nor was it the beautiful new church with a red-tiled roof, which could be seen for many miles around the valley.

Perhaps because she had not always been a Mission Indian, Pasquala enjoyed Mission life more than her friends María, Elena, and Barbara. But it was mostly because of jolly Father Uría that Pasquala sang and laughed so frequently. She loved the jokes and teasing of the stout, kind-hearted padre, who had once been a soldier and who still walked like one, in spite of his long gray robe.

"Everyone of us is a soldier, Pasquala," he surprised her by saying. "We all have enemies to fight."

Pasquala glanced up into his twinkling, brown eyes to see whether this were some new joke. But as they entered the Mission church, the dimmer light inside made it difficult for her to tell what he meant. As usual, Pasquala stopped a moment to admire the statue of Santa Inés, after whom the Mission was named.

"Surely Santa Inés was not a soldier," the child said wonderingly.

The padre nodded his head. "Ah, but she was a Christian soldier!" he insisted. "See, this statue holds a lamb in one hand to show the Saint's gentleness. But the other hand is gripping a sword. Santa Inés gave her life for her church when she was a little older than you are now, Pasquala. She was a very brave girl."

Outside in the sunshine once more, the Indian girl trembled a moment as she thought of what the padre had said. Her deep-set, dark-brown eyes glowed with a new-found courage. "I would give my life for the Mission, too, Padre!"

Father Uría put his arm around the child, who had suddenly grown serious. "Now, now, Pasquala," he coaxed. "No need for the girl we call the 'Sunshine of the Mission' to think of such things." He chuckled as he continued, "Besides, don't you remember how long it took me to nurse you back to health when you came here sick a few years ago?

No more of that, let me tell you!" He shook his
fist at her playfully.

Pasquala burst out laughing to see his round fist
close to her nose. She laughed until her long black
hair, loosened from its strip of red cotton ribbon,
came tumbling down over her round, brown face
and hid her dark eyes. How well she remembered
those days. She had been sick after her first trip
over the mountains from her own Tulare country.
Her people had come to the wide ocean beach to
fish and to gather shells. How was she to know
that feasting on mussels, clams, crabs, and other
shellfish would make her very ill?

Fortunately her parents had reached Santa Inés
Mission in time to put her under the padre's gentle
care. All the rest of her people had gone home again,
across the mountains, leaving Pasquala and her
father and mother behind. It was weeks before the
child was out of danger. She was thankful that her
family had become Mission Indians. Her recovery
still seemed like a miracle to her.

Pasquala had learned from the Mexican women
to make cornmeal tortillas, big and round and thin,
like pancakes. She and María and the other girls
gathered apples, peaches, and grapes from the Mission orchard.

Every afternoon Pasquala played with her Indian friends. Sometimes they went on picnics down to the ocean beach, several miles away. Often the children cooked fresh clams on hot rocks at the beach, but several years passed before Pasquala would taste shellfish again.

During the mornings there was work for even the smallest Mission child. The deep-toned bells called them very early from their beds to the service at the church, where they could join in the singing and the prayers. Sometimes Pasquala's eyes wandered upward to the bright decorations the Indian workmen had painted on the ceilings and walls. Many times, during the songs, Pasquala looked at the statue of little Santa Inés and wondered about the lamb and the sword she carried. Sometimes on wintry mornings when Pasquala was scarcely awake, she thought Santa Inés smiled at her or joined in the songs.

After the chapel service Pasquala did not always wait to be told to work. She would scamper straight to the padre. "Do you want us to watch the sheep?" she asked one day.

"Of course," laughed Father Uría. "We are short of shepherds just now, but the sheep won't mind if we have girl sheepherders."

The other girls scolded Pasquala for her eagerness to work. "Maybe we could have played instead of working," María suggested.

"Or perhaps we could have picked grapes or helped in the kitchens where they were cooking good food," added plump little Barbara, who always liked to nibble.

Whatever the work happened to be for the day, whether gardening, spinning, weaving, or sewing, Pasquala sang while she worked. No wonder everyone loved her and called her the "Sunshine of the Mission!"

Feast days were holidays. Christmas, Easter, Candlemas Day, and Rosary Sunday were all special days, but the feast day of Santa Inés on January twenty-first was very special. The Indian musicians tuned up their finest instruments for the celebration. The flute, horn, tambour, and triangle played music that echoed and re-echoed across the beautiful narrow valley.

Behind the Indian village of eighty white adobe houses with red-tiled, gabled roofs was a large square, or plaza, to which came all the best horsemen for many miles. Mexican rancheros who had settled near the Mission, Spanish and Mexican soldiers of the guard, and trained Indian horsemen

dressed in gay fiesta costumes—all rode their well-groomed horses to the plaza.

The little girls kept well out of the way while watching the races. When the time came for "tailing the bull," they hurried away to play their own games. They climbed the tall willows and white sycamores along the banks of the rushing river, which was swollen by winter rains. But the girls were curious about "tailing the bull" and the cock chase, and before long they returned to the village to hear about them.

"That was a stubborn bull," Pasquala's father muttered.

María's half-frightened eyes were round and shining. "Was it the poor old bull that is usually in the north pasture?" she whispered.

"The very same," nodded the father. "The horsemen had to prod him with sticks to make him angry. When they opened a gate to let him out, all the riders pursued him at full speed. The first one who reached him grabbed the bull by the tail and twisted it until the beast rolled over in the dirt. How the crowd roared and cheered!"

The girls were silent. Pasquala was glad they had not seen the chase. The music and dancing would please them far more.

Toward dusk the dancers gathered in the center of the Plaza. The musicians and all the other Indians formed a circle around them. Some of the Indian dancers were painted in bright colors just as in the days before the coming of the padres. Round and round they danced, far into the night, sometimes slow, sometimes fast. For some of the dances the children clapped their hands in time to the whistle or rattle.

Feasting continued during the fiesta days. Cattle were plentiful at the time, and the cooks barbecued the meat in deep pits and seasoned it with rich spices and sauces. The padres would sell the hides to trading vessels from Boston.

In certain years spring came early to this sheltered valley and brought with it such tall wild flowers that the children could hide in them.

One day while playing in a field of golden poppies close to the Mission, Pasquala saw the padre preparing to make a trip over the mountains.

"Please let me go with you," she called.

Father Uría shook his head. "No, my child! You stay here at the Mission and work and play. Some of the Indians back in your home valley are very fierce. They do not like white men or Mission Indians."

"Then do not go into that country," begged Pasquala. "Nothing must happen to you!"

The padre sighed. "The good God will watch over me. Some of your people need my help. Remember, my child, we are always soldiers."

Many times the children went into the church to pray for the padre's safe return. Before long their prayers were answered, and the jolly padre came back to the Mission. Several families of Tulare Indians followed him, some of them with children Pasquala had known when she was very small.

There was always something new to show these strangers, who were studying to become Mission Indians. Big new paintings and new statues had arrived for the church. But there was no new statue so important to Pasquala as the lovely little one of Santa Inés. María, Elena, and Barbara helped her to make the new children feel at home. Pasquala's mother taught their mothers how to spin and weave, while her father, who was now overseer of the gardens, taught their fathers how to make ditches to irrigate the vast orchards and vegetable gardens.

"We grow food all summer long," Pasquala boasted. Then she showed the children the irrigation lines that carried water from the mountain springs and streams to the thirsty summer gardens.

Although the new children had marveled at all the other wonders of the Mission, they opened their eyes still wider when they saw the green gardens in summer. The Tulare country had no irrigation, only rainfall, and quite soon after the coming of warm weather, everything there became dry and brown.

In September the Mission vineyards were a sight worth seeing. Huge clusters of purple grapes hung down from vines which were beginning to turn yellow and red. The padre called for old and young to come out into the sunshine and pick the ripe fruit.

Dressed in her favorite red skirt and blue blouse, Pasquala picked grapes near the road. She sang a happy song as she worked beside her mother, who was not strong enough to carry her own heavy basket. Near by, Pasquala's father was showing the other Indians where to pick first. Above the sound of her singing, Pasquala heard the noise of pounding hoofbeats. Her father looked up.

"The Tulares! The Tulares!" he shouted, pointing to a band of Indians who were riding full speed toward the vineyards on their stolen Mission horses.

An arrow silenced her father's warning shouts. The first rider, slackening his speed but little, scooped up Pasquala in his arms. The second rider

snatched up her mother and rode away. Other riders circled the Mission and shot arrows toward the people in the vineyard.

Pasquala kicked and struggled until her captors tied her hands and feet. "Please let us return home to the Mission!" she kept crying, until they put a gag tightly across her mouth.

"Far better you return home to country of Tulares," muttered the rider. "Mission padres make nothing but trouble for our people."

Pasquala tried to protest, but her gag held tight. The band of Indians rode through the pastures, across the river, through the orchards, and up the mountain trail. At the summit they stopped a moment to rest their horses. Far out to the west were the blue waters of the Pacific. But down in the valley, where leaves were beginning to add their yellow, brown, red, and gold to the somber evergreens along the hillsides, were the red-tiled roofs of the lovely Mission buildings. A sob choked Pasquala. The rider laughed harshly.

"Say good-by to your paleface Mission! Never will you see it again."

Pasquala could not speak. She could not even give her mother any words of comfort. But she could murmur a silent prayer.

"Dear God of the Missions! Help me to be brave! Please let me return some day to the Mission I love!"

The rider kicked his horse and led the band down the steep trail on the other side of the mountain. Miles and miles they rode, up one slope and down another, across nearly dry streams, and over flat, brown country. At night when they reached the end of the journey, the Indians took Pasquala and her mother down from the horses and dropped them, none too gently, before a deserted tule hut.

They had had no food since early morning. They found no bed to sleep on and no blankets to protect them from the chill of evening. But they were so exhausted that they slept until the blue jays wakened them in the morning with harsh, insistent chatter.

Stiff and sore from her long journey and from her sleep on the bare ground, Pasquala crept quietly out of the hut and away from the village, in search of food for her mother. She found nothing but wild blackberries and a few wild nuts. Later in the day an Indian woman gave her a strip of dried venison.

"Do not tell," she warned Pasquala. "Our village council very angry that so many Tulare Indians go to Mission."

Before Pasquala could be quite sure of her mean-

ing, the woman had slipped away into her own hut. But her kindness revived both captives even more than the food.

Pasquala looked about her. The Indian village was not the one in which she and her mother had lived before they had gone to the Mission. In fact, neither of them knew where they were. The cone-shaped huts, arranged in a straight row, were made of poles and tules woven together. Some of them had tule-rush mats to cover the doorway.

Pasquala thought of the comfortable beds, the tables and benches in their white adobe Mission house, and she longed for a comfortable bed for her mother. Winter rains would soon come, and where could she get blankets and nourishing food for herself and her mother? Pasquala knew she must face these problems before long. She missed the gay companionship of the children and the jolly padre, and the inspiration of the Mission.

Pasquala soon learned that her captors intended no harm to her, but that they expected her to work. She had to gather food not only for herself but for them. Although her mother was not well enough to venture from the hut, she was able to weave fine baskets of willows.

In a few days Pasquala gathered load after load

of acorns, which her mother cracked and ground into meal on a flat rock. To remove the bitterness, she "leached" the acorn meal by soaking it for many days in wet sand. Pasquala gathered nuts, wild grapes, and berries, and offered part of them to her kind neighbor, Tacchel, in return for meat. While Pasquala was away hunting food and tules, her mother wove tule mats and capes for extra warmth during the colder weather that was already upon them.

"You know many wonderful things to do, Mother, dear!" Pasquala said, for she admired her mother's courage during this time of hardship. "Many of these things we did not learn at the Mission."

Her mother sighed. "Yes, my child. Long before the coming of the padres, the Indians learned to provide." The mother glanced at the girl's tangled hair. "Since we lost our combs on the trip across the mountains, I must make you a new comb or a hairbrush."

"But how?" Pasquala laughed for the first time in many days.

"First you must find me some soaproot," her mother explained. "With part of it we can wash our hair until it shines like a crow's wing. Then I shall wash the soaproot thoroughly and separate its root-

lets. When I tie them to a small piece of wood they will be like the fine brushes used by the Mexican señoritas at the Mission village."

Pasquala resolved that if her mother could make the best of things, she, too, must be as happy and cheerful as possible. The soaproot made good soap for their hair, and the brushes combed out the tangles. Tule fibers were surely as good as red ribbons for tying the hair in place. She had no mirrors except quiet streams to show whether they were as pretty.

At last came the shortest day of the year. Pasquala knew that one moon later would be Santa Inés Day. When the day came, she and her mother sang the Mission songs and talked of the dancing and the great barbecue at the Mission. Pasquala marked the date on a near-by scrub oak so that she could keep account of the passing time. Often she thought about trying to escape to the Mission. There were several horses tied up at the other end of the village, but she knew her mother could never stand the trip across the mountains.

Later in the spring the Tulare Indians ordered Pasquala to go on a fishing expedition to a distant stream with some of the villagers. The neighboring Indian woman, Tacchel, whom Pasquala had taught

to sing several of the Mission songs, promised to look after Pasquala's mother.

Such a strange way of fishing! Pasquala carried the nets, made of milkweed fiber, to the edge of a pool while the men put soaproot into the water and stirred it with sticks. In a short time the poison of the root had stunned the fish and the Indians scooped them up in the net. Pasquala thought this was not quite fair to the fish, but the Indians needed food. When she had dried her share of the fish, she had a good supply for months to come.

Another rainy season came. Pasquala marked another Santa Inés Day beside the first. It was hard for her to believe in a Mission God when the Mission was so far away. But she must sing the songs and be cheerful for the sake of her mother. Sometimes it seemed as if they had always been living in this Tulare Indian village and as though the Mission were only a wonderful dream.

Her mother grew weaker. Pasquala knew that her mother would be glad to leave for the heaven of the padres. The girl cut another gouge in the scrub oak to mark the third Santa Inés Day since they had been captured. This fiesta day was in the year 1824 of the Mission calendar.

Before the passing of another moon, a day came

when Pasquala heard many horses. She saw riders gallop past her hut, and she noticed the Mission brand on their horses. As soon as Tacchel could stay with her mother, the girl hurried out to the village for news of her beloved Mission. The strangers' horses were all tied securely in a row with three armed Indians guarding them. That was strange! Very strange! But Pasquala did not linger there. On to the council hut she fled. Even before she reached it she could hear loud voices.

"Our revenge very good," laughed one of the newcomers.

"Padres think Indians forget!" shouted another. "But in two days we all meet together and attack Mission Santa Inés first! Kill! Burn! Destroy!"

Pasquala waited to hear no more. She glanced at the horses; then she shook her head. No chance of taking a horse with all those guards! She would have to walk. Outside her hut she met Tacchel.

"Your mother has gone to the land from which Indians never return. Before she left she said for you to go to the Mission! Hurry," her friend whispered.

Tears came to Pasquala's eyes. Then she bowed her head to murmur a Mission prayer. She had no time to grieve for her mother. Instead, she was

thankful that her mother had been spared further suffering.

Gratefully Pasquala took the long, thin strip of dry venison and the small bag of acorn meal that Tacchel gave her. She would not be missed until morning. Maybe not then. She looked at the distant mountain, shrouded in a purple-blue haze. Somewhere in the general direction of the setting sun was Mission Santa Inés. She dared not follow any trail at first lest she be discovered.

Barefoot, clad in nothing but a thin tule skirt, Pasquala started to run. As long as she ran she did not notice the cold February evening. But she could not keep running very long at a time. Half-running, half-walking, she scurried through vines, bushes, and streams. A low tule fog engulfed her and made her uncertain of her direction. Hour by hour it grew colder until dawn. Even the sun, after it rose, brought little warmth for several hours.

As far as she could see there was no one following her. She chewed some of the dried venison and ate a little acorn meal, but her throat was so parched she could scarcely swallow. At last she found a stream and drank deeply of its icy water. On and on she went. Even in the light of day she could not tell where she was. She knew only that she must climb

those towering mountains. During the very warmest part of the day she rested for an hour in a sheltered spot. She must go on! On! On!

By evening she had followed a twisting canyon through the lower hills. But she could find no easy pass through the higher mountains. The sun disappeared behind them early, leaving an immediate chill where the slope had been warm before.

Up, up, up she climbed. The undergrowth was so dense and the vines so thorny that her legs and arms were scratched and raw. Climbing was slower and slower. If only she had a trail to follow instead of this route over rocks and thorns and brambles!

Her feet were bruised and swollen. She was chilled by the cold night, without shelter, without sleep, and without sufficient food. How could she hope to reach the Mission in time?

A coyote crossed her path, more startled than she was. A hungry mountain lion howled dismally from the summit of the mountain. Pasquala shivered and trembled. Often she tripped and fell headlong, but always she got up and staggered on. A biting wind stirred the trees. But fortunately it also blew away the clouds that were hiding the moon.

"Light the way for me," she murmured as she saw the thin moon high above her.

Far up toward the top of the mountain, the moon's beams shone on a yucca in full bloom, weeks, yes, months, ahead of its season. In a moment Pasquala was on her knees.

"The yucca!" she cried. "It is the 'candle of the Lord,' or so they name it at the Mission!" From her parched lips poured the almost forgotten, fervent Mission prayers. Then she added her own special plea. "Dear Father! Show me the way! Show me the way!"

A gurgling stream called to her, and she bathed her aching feet for a few moments. She had new strength, new courage, new faith. She fought her way, step by step, up the steep mountain. By daybreak she had reached the summit. Out beyond her stretched the great Pacific.

The western, grassy slopes were less difficult. She slid and tumbled down through the blue grassnuts and golden poppies.

"*Copa de oro*," she murmured to the poppies that were just opening to the sun. " 'Cup of gold' the padres call them, or 'sleepy ones' because they close up at night."

Pasquala's head ached from the bumps, the bruises, and the falls, but mostly from lack of sleep. She could keep going now. She must keep going

for the few hours it would take her to reach the Mission. At last she found a trail—the very trail the riders had used when they took her captive. It would save time to use it now.

Running, slipping, falling, she hurried down the narrow path. Almost stumbling headlong at a sharp turn, she saw at last the gleaming red tiles of the Mission buildings. Then she was not too late!

Down in the valley she began to run. She tried to call out when she saw the beloved, jolly padre. But no words would come. Her running feet attracted his attention.

"Pasquala! My Pasquala!" he cried.

But Pasquala could run no farther. She fell at his feet. "Padre! Padre!" she gasped. "Tulare Indians are coming! Send word to other Missions!"

The padre carried Pasquala to her own little bed. But on the way he gave sharp orders to the soldiers. "Arm every soldier of the guard! Prepare every Mission Indian for attack! Send messengers to Santa Barbara and Purísima Missions!"

Tenderly he wrapped the thin girl in warm blankets and listened to her few, drowsy words. "Is Santa Inés safe?"

"The Mission is safe, my child! And our own little Santa Inés still stands in the chapel. She will

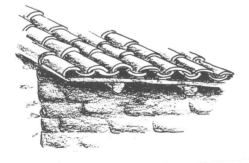

surely give you her richest blessing! Pasquala, my child, you are indeed a most worthy Christian soldier. You have risked your life for your Mission!"

"Thank you, Padre," Pasquala murmured sleepily. "I am so glad to be home in my own bed."

The Anger of Chupu

Mission La Purísima Concepción

INTRODUCTION

TWO MEN were dear to the heart of Francisco, the Mission Indian boy. One of them was Father Payéras, the understanding padre at Mission Purísima Concepción. The other was the boy's grandfather, a powerful Indian chief. Francisco hoped to persuade his grandfather to come to the Mission to live. But between the stern chieftain and the Mission was the "anger of Chupu."

At the time of this story, Purísima Mission was almost twenty-five years old. It was founded in 1787, the eleventh in the chain of twenty-one. The Mission was located near the ocean between Missions San Luis Obispo and Santa Barbara. Although winter floods often damaged the new Mission, it began to prosper. The padres taught the Chumash Indians to build fine adobe structures roofed with red tile. They built dams and aqueducts to control the water and to irrigate the large orchards and gardens.

In 1804 Father Payéras came to Purísima Mission and remained there until his death nineteen years later. After he had learned the Indian language he translated some of the prayers in order to help the newer Mission Indians understand them. Within two years after his arrival, the number of Mission Indians had increased until they reached a peak of fifteen hundred.

It was not only among his Indians that Father Payéras was popular. The other padres in California admired him, and the military authorities found him agreeable. After he had been at this Mission for a few years, he was appointed president of all the California Missions. Although he continued to live at Purísima, he visited other Missions and tried to reach Indians in the mountains and valleys beyond the Missions. The year before he died, he made the long, tiring journey to the Russian settlement at Fort Ross. His years as supervisor of all the Missions were difficult years, yet because of the wisdom and devotion of Father Payéras there was no real clash with military authorities.

During this time Purísima Mission flourished. The Mission Indians were raising fine palomino horses successfully. Indians from the mountains around the Mission were turning away from the worship of Achup, or Chupu, their jealous Indian god, and coming to the Mission.

Then without warning came the earthquake of 1812. It destroyed the Mission and left a hundred Indian homes in ruins. It split open the mountain behind the Mission, and from this gap poured black sand and water, adding to the destruction. Indians fled in terror to the hills, convinced that this tragedy was a warning from Chupu.

The earthquake of 1812 damaged many of the Missions. Less severe shocks occurred from time to time. Frequently they cracked heavy adobe walls, knocked down towers, and made buildings unsafe until they were repaired. The California Indians had experienced many earthquakes, but they considered any unusual act of Nature as a sign from their angry gods. The native houses, made of branches, tules, and mud, were not greatly disturbed by earthquakes. But Mission houses, of very thick adobe, cracked readily and fell into ruins. This increased the Indians' fear of their native god and added to the problems of the padres.

After the earthquake of 1812, Father Payéras moved Purísima Mission to a new site. Gradually the Indians returned. But drought, fire, and disease next troubled the Mission. The Indians helped to build a new adobe church, and then in a few years enemy Indians attacked in full force. Seculari-

zation soon followed, bringing with it the usual neglect of Mission property. The Mission was sold but was later returned to the Catholic Church.

The buildings had fallen into almost complete ruins. Then in 1935 the state of California began restoration of the Mission and its 507 acres of land as a state park. Whenever possible, the workmen used old materials and rebuilt, following the original design and plans. Today, visitors can see the new church, like the one where Mission Indians worshiped with the padres, and fountains like those where Indian women did their washing. Back of the Mission stands the hill which split wide open at the time of the dreadful earthquake and terrified the Indians with its evidence of the "anger of Chupu."

CALENDAR

1787 Founding of the Mission, December 8
1804 Coming of Father Payéras
1812 The earthquake
1818 Erection of the new adobe church
1845 Sale of the Mission
1874 Return of the Mission to the Catholic Church
1935 Beginning of the restoration of the Mission as
      a state park

THE ANGER OF CHUPU

𝔉 RANCISCO stood beside the young palomino horse. But while he brushed its well-shaped head and combed its cream-colored mane and tail, he was not thinking of the horse. His thoughts had wandered far from Purísima Mission to the high mountain where his grandfather lived. If only this proud and dignified old chief would come to the Mission to live, Francisco would be completely happy! Almost every week he visited his grandfather, but somehow Francisco could never find just the right words to persuade him to come to the Mission. Now that Francisco was all alone, currying the nearly full-grown horse, he thought of something convincing to say.

"You belong here with me, Grandfather," he said aloud, between strokes of the stiff brush. "Don't you see? You are all the family I have, and I am all that is left for you. The padre will give you one of the new adobe houses, where we can live together always and take care of each other."

The boy was so intent on his work that he did

73

not notice the arrival of Father Payéras until a shadow fell across the horse.

"How sleek and shiny young Monte is!" The padre's brown eyes twinkled as he added, "But what was that you were telling him about living in an adobe house?"

The boy laughed merrily. "Not Monte in an adobe house, Padre! It is my grandfather. I keep hoping he will come to the Mission."

The padre nodded gravely. "It is hard for older men to change their ways. The chief of a Chumash village will not easily give up his position of authority and start a new life. But have faith, my son. Other chieftains have found the Mission ways are good ways and the Mission God is the God of love."

The boy sighed as he continued his work. He knew that Chief Neuia was no ordinary chieftain. "Grandfather has a mind of his own," he muttered.

"Yes, son," agreed the padre, who had been at the Mission for as long as Francisco could remember. "Every leader must have a mind of his own, but to be really great he must also listen to a higher wisdom." The padre paused a moment, then continued gravely, "People are like horses. They may be full of strength and courage, yet they need discipline and training if they are to be useful. And, speaking

of horses, did you know that a ranchero had offered much money for Monte?"

Francisco's heart almost stopped beating. His dark eyes questioned Father Payéras. The boy had always felt sure of the padre's wisdom and kindness. During all the years the padre had been teaching the Indians valuable skills, he himself had labored in the fields or shops, and every Indian had learned to trust him. So whatever he decided must be for the best. "What—what did you tell him?" Francisco whispered at last.

"Just that Monte was not for sale," the padre said slowly. "I'm sure you will have him well trained by early December, when you celebrate your birthday. After that I have important plans for you, my son. We have no other young Indian as good with horses. Although you are young, I plan to place you in charge of all the palomino horses and let you have Monte for your own use."

No words came to the boy's lips. Instead, he knelt beside the beloved padre and waited for the words of encouragement that always followed his blessing. "We need more Indians like you, Francisco—dependable and hard working. And don't forget, my son, that the Mission God is always ready to help you with your problems."

"Thank you, Padre. Many thanks," murmured the boy. "And may I go to visit my grandfather soon?"

Father Payéras nodded in answer to the boy's eager request. "Go now, lad! And tell Chief Neuia we shall be glad at any time to have him visit us."

Francisco led Monte into a corral where there was plenty of hay and fresh water. Then after washing himself hurriedly in a small stream, he ran along the grassy path. He climbed the steep slope to the mountaintop where he could look out over the Pacific Ocean far below him. The boy's bare feet made almost no sound as he approached his grandfather's hut in the Indian village. But when he pushed aside the tule mat hanging from the doorway, the old man called out to him.

"Enter, my son! I awaited your coming!"

The boy sat down on the floor opposite his grandfather and looked up into the keen eyes that glowed with affection as well as with pride. Chief Neuia was tall and sturdy as a mature pine tree. His long black hair showed no sign of graying; his dark face was weather-beaten and roughened from outdoor life and seaward excursions. His stern mouth grew softer as he watched his young visitor.

"Today," the Chief began, "Chief Neuia has

much to tell you! But first—we eat." A note of scorn crept into his low voice as he added, "Mission food is no good for council talk."

With great ceremony he handed the boy a highly polished wooden bowl. Around the outside of it were inlaid small pieces of abalone shell in a shrimp design. After Francisco had admired the design, a young Indian placed a roasted quail and baked seed cakes in the bowl.

The boy and his grandfather ate in silence. Although Francisco had no fear of the great Chief, he respected him and knew that he must wait for him to speak first.

The Chief pushed aside his bowl and motioned to Francisco to do the same. "Good food! Good dishes! Good company!" The man's dark eyes glowed. "All my family are gone—sons—daughters—gone from my house." His eyes wandered around the room, which at one time had sheltered twenty people. "Empty house! You share it with me. Then I am never lonely."

As Chief Neuia paused, his grandson spoke quickly. "But I am a Mission Indian! I was born in the Mission village, and only today the padre—"

The boy was silenced by a motion of the chieftain's hand. "Chief Neuia speaks," the man said

gravely. "My village must plan for a new chief—a Young Chief! He must train for many years."

Francisco was deeply impressed by his grandfather's words, for he knew that every Indian in the village longed to be chief. Yet his grandfather was offering him the honor. Again the boy tried to speak, and again he was silenced while the chieftain told him about a fishing trip he had planned and about the evening worship of Chupu.

Francisco had no chance to refuse the invitation or to tell about his own plans at the Mission. Instead he followed his grandfather and four braves down the trail to the ocean, where a long, well-built canoe was hidden in a lagoon. Gravely, Chief Neuia pointed to a place at the bow where the boy was to sit. The chieftain sat at the stern. Then the four stalwart Indian youths began to whirl their bladed paddles in and out of the water.

Francisco enjoyed his first trip out on the ocean. It had been smooth enough in the lagoon, but outside, the breakers were piling up in great waves and dashing high over the shore. Skillfully the paddlers waited until three very large breakers had lashed the rocks and beach; then they paddled quickly through the smaller waves and sped out beyond the surf.

As the canoe reached the calmer water where

only the regular swells rocked it gently, Francisco examined his grandfather's boat. It was made of long, shaped planks fitted carefully together, lashed with sinew or plant fiber, and waterproofed at the seams with an asphalt mixture found along the beach. The craft might well hold twenty Indians, yet a few could paddle it easily. The boy rubbed his hand gently over the smoothly polished prow of the boat and traced with his fingers the pattern of inlaid shells.

At a signal from Chief Neuia the paddlers stopped near a rocky point, and one gave the boy a fishing line with an almost circular hook. Silently all the Indians except the chieftain fished for the perch, smelt, and mackerel that were biting not far below the surface. In a short time a large catch of the shimmering fish lay in the bottom of the canoe. Chief Neuia separated Francisco's fish from the others. "You shall not eat of your own catch," he warned the boy. "It would spoil your luck."

Again Chief Neuia spoke to Francisco. "Take one of the paddles. See what you can do."

The boy had watched the other Indians, but he found paddling very difficult, almost as difficult as learning to know the paces of a horse. Slowly and awkwardly the canoe approached shore. Francisco

tightened his hold on the paddle when he noticed the breaker line just ahead. But at that instant the more experienced paddlers took charge and waited for the lull before rushing through the surf.

The sun was setting far out across the sea by the time Chief Neuia and the boy reached the village again. They began to cook the freshly cleaned fish on rocks heated in the fire outside the hut. Still no word was spoken. The boy was eager to talk about the Mission, but whenever he started to speak he was silenced. From the distant mountaintop he could hear the shrill music of bone whistles and the weird chants of voices. The Indians were preparing for their evening ceremony.

Slowly the Chief and the boy climbed the slippery, pine-needle path, their way lighted only by the stars and a pale crescent moon. Even in his woolen clothing Francisco felt strangely chilled as he caught glimpses of painted figures creeping silently along other paths. At a freshly swept clearing on the summit, he saw a circle of Indians waiting for their chieftain and their medicine man. In the center, near the tall poles decorated with brightly colored feathers, the musicians played for the slowly swaying dancers.

From the outside circle, Francisco watched mem-

bers of the village council, standing with hands full of seeds, acorns, and wild fruits. He saw Chief Neuia walk with great dignity to his place. Then the music and dancing ceased. The voice of the Chief rang out in a deep, reverent chant.

"Captain of Captains, behold us! Hear what we say!"

The voices of the people chanting in a chorus added their part to the ceremony. As the men of the council stepped forward they offered their seeds, acorns, and wild fruits. Prayers were said for rain, for the harvest, and for good health. Again came the shrill whistle and the mournful music of singers.

Francisco was thankful when at last his grandfather joined him and they started down the path toward the village. Inside the large house the boy shivered until the Chief placed a warm fur cloak over his shoulders and pointed to a platform covered by a woven tule mat. Silently the old man walked over to his own platform, pulled aside the tule curtain, and disappeared behind it.

For a while Francisco lay there quietly. But he felt restless and uncomfortable on the strange bed in his grandfather's house. How was he going to make the Chief understand his reasons for not leaving the Mission?

The next morning while they ate breakfast in the warm sunshine, the Chief was in a more talkative mood.

"My people need you," he said again. "Chupu is a jealous god! Chupu's anger is terrible!"

Francisco decided he had been patient and respectful long enough. "My Mission needs me," he said slowly. "The Mission God is a God of love, but He asks obedience too." Without giving the Chief a chance to reply, the boy continued, "The padre has important work for everyone in the Mission. He offers you one of the new adobe huts, just big enough for the two of us. And he has promised to put me in charge of the palominos in December and to let me ride Monte anywhere."

The Chief shook his head. "Who are palominos? Who is Monte?"

Francisco was glad he had a chance to answer these questions. "Palominos are horses chosen by kings. They are horses with light manes and light tails. They bring much money from rancheros. Our Mission raises the finest in all California, and Monte is the most wonderful of all."

"Humph!" grunted the Chief. "We buy you this Monte horse when you come here."

The boy sighed. He knew that his grandfather

would promise him almost anything if only he would stay in the mountains. But how could he ever persuade the Chief to come to the Mission? "Please come to the Mission, Grandfather," he begged. "The padre is kind and understanding. The Mission God answers prayers of white men and Indians."

Chief Neuia's eyes narrowed. "Does the Mission God send rain and good harvest?"

For a moment the boy hesitated. Only too well he remembered the years when gardens had suffered because no rain had fallen. Then he remembered something else, far more important. "The padre and the Indians have built a large cement-lined ditch to bring water down from the mountain streams," he said proudly. "Our Mission God teaches us not only to pray for what we need, but to work for it too. We have learned not to depend on rain or the wild harvest. At the Mission we plant our own grain. We grow all the fruit and vegetables we need."

But Chief Neuia shook his head. Then after a few moments he said sadly, "Chupu is jealous god. Chumash ways are not Mission ways."

There was an awkward pause. The boy felt somehow that this was not the best time to tell

more about the Mission God. Nor was it the time to describe the wonderful celebrations at the Mission—the horse races, the bull-and-bear fights, the cock chase, and the feasting and dancing. One look at the Chief told Francisco how he had disappointed his grandfather by refusing to leave the Mission. There seemed nothing more that he could say.

When the sun was high in the sky, the boy started homeward down the trail. His step was slow. He was deep in thought. At the last bend in the path he glanced up and saw the Chief standing alone.

Back again at the Mission, Francisco became so busy with plans for his new work that he did not go to the mountains for several weeks. Warm summer days made some Indians lazy, but not Francisco and his helpers. They began work long before the heat of the day, fencing a pasture for the horses and building them a wooden shelter covered with thick adobe.

Francisco was very proud of these golden palominos at the Mission. Each year the little band was increasing. Rancheros from Santa Barbara, San Gabriel, and Monterey stopped at Purísima Mission to rest overnight and to partake of Mission hospitality. Before starting off again at daybreak, many

of them rode out to the new pasture to admire the palominos.

Frequently one of the rancheros offered a good price for Monte. Although Francisco dreaded these offers for his horse, he always put Monte through paces which showed the graceful lines of his neck and head, his gentleness and quick obedience to his young master, and also his sensitivity to a stranger's touch.

Francisco longed to spend all his time with these wonderful horses, but he had other tasks at the Mission. He helped to build new adobe houses for Indians who had come from distant villages. Each time he completed a new house, whitewashed inside and out and fitted up with wooden bunks, Francisco thought of his grandfather in the lonely house on the mountaintop. Whenever the boy sang new chants with the Mission choir and orchestra, his voice rang out joyfully until he remembered the chorus on the mountaintop chanting to the shrill music of the bone whistle. Then he no longer cared to sing.

Even when Francisco helped to harvest the crops from the Mission orchards, feeling pride in the beautiful fruit, the memory of his grandfather's scorn of Mission ways would pass through his mind. But

when he took his turn at the altar and helped Father Payéras in the wonderful services of the church, he forgot for a time everything but his great love for the Mission and the Mission God.

One morning when he was dressed in his holiday clothes, he went into the church and said a special prayer for his beloved grandfather. Suddenly a new determination swept through him—a determination to persuade Chief Neuia somehow, some way, to come to the Mission for a visit. The moment the service was finished, he hurried to the padre's little room.

"May I ride up the mountain to see my grandfather?" he asked. "Perhaps if he sees Monte he will decide to come back with me."

Father Payéras smiled encouragingly at the boy. "Go, my son," he said. "Surely some day your faith will bring a reward!"

With a nod of thanks the boy ran down to the pasture. He curried the horse until its coat shone like gold in the sunshine. As he rode away toward the hills, Francisco was proud of his own appearance too. His clothes were of blue wool, carded, woven, and tailored in the Mission shops. He had combed his black hair carefully and smoothed it back with a little tallow grease to keep it from blowing over

his eyes. His merry brown face shone, partly because of the thorough scrubbing he had given it and partly because of his great pride in being allowed to ride Monte away from the Mission grounds.

How different the trip seemed when he was riding! On the narrow turns at the edge of the cliff the horse hugged the bank. This time his approach to the village attracted a crowd of excited Indians. Chief Neuia was standing outside his hut.

"Is it—really you, my boy?" his grandfather asked, shading his eyes as he stared up at the rider.

Francisco smiled, aware of the pride in the chieftain's voice. "Your grandson, Chief Neuia!" he cried as he dismounted and led the horse to the door of the large hut. Slowly the chieftain walked all the way around the beautiful palomino, careful to keep at a distance. Then he came close to the boy.

"Is that Monte?" he asked.

Francisco nodded. "How would you like to ride him back to the Mission?"

The Chief hesitated, then looked furtively about at his people, still watching from their doorways. The boy noticed this and spoke again. "Father Payéras sent you a special invitation, Chief Neuia. Please ride back with me to the Mission!"

"Chupu is jealous god," the Chief muttered

under his breath. Then a new gleam shone in his eyes. "Do others ride Monte?" he asked.

"No one else has ridden him," said Francisco. "But Monte will be honored to have you ride." As he spoke, he stepped over to the horse, stroked its nose, and whispered, "You will, won't you, Monte?" As if in reply the horse nodded its head vigorously while the boy smoothed out the finely woven blanket on which his grandfather was to sit.

Now that the Chief had decided to ride to the Mission he seemed in high spirits. After mounting the horse he called out a loud signal that brought his villagers running to his side.

"Chief Neuia will ride to Mission!" he announced.

It was all that Francisco could do to keep the nervous horse quiet in the midst of the excited crowd. Nor did it help when the village medicine man strode close to Monte's head and muttered in a dreadful chant, "Chupu angry! Chupu — jealous god!"

But at a nod from Chief Neuia, the boy led the horse through the crowd and down to the beginning of the trail. Then Francisco gave the reins to his grandfather while he himself walked along the trail ahead of the horse. No word was spoken between

them on the trip, yet the boy knew from the man's expression that he was enjoying every moment.

At last the Mission was in sight. Francisco felt a glow of pride as he gazed at the dazzling white adobe huts in the Indian village and at the bright red tiles that covered all the buildings. To him it was home. But a gasp from his grandfather revealed that the Chief found it a new and amazing world. As they crossed the stream and came nearer to the Mission, the bells pealed out their call to evening worship. The horse broke into a trot that jogged Chief Neuia up and down.

As soon as they reached the pasture and the new shelter, Francisco led the horse inside. Then he took his grandfather to meet the padre, who was just leaving his bare room for the church. The two men, similar in height and build but unlike in appearance and background, faced each other a moment. Then they smiled and nodded. Chief Neuia's arm was raised in friendly greeting and the padre's arm in blessing. Although the words of each were unfamiliar to the other, Francisco knew there was real admiration between these two men whom he loved best in all the world.

The boy and his grandfather went to the church service and knelt side by side, surrounded by hun-

dreds of other Indians. Never before had the chapel seemed so warm and friendly, so full of the kindly spirit of the padres who had founded it and had served its people now for twenty-five years. After the chants and prayers were finished, Francisco walked out proudly beside Chief Neuia. In the gathering dusk the boy showed the Chief the splendor of the Mission and the beauty of the Indian village. But the eager chatter was silenced by a gesture.

"Chupu is jealous god," Chief Neuia muttered. Abruptly he turned away from the boy. "Mission is for white men! Chupu is for Chumash."

Without another word the Chief strode toward the path that led to his mountain home. Amazed and heartbroken, the boy watched him disappear from sight. Francisco realized at last that not all the glory of the Mission could tempt the Chief to forsake the sort of life he had known so long.

Sometimes, during the days that followed, Francisco found it difficult to have faith. He had done his best to persuade his grandfather to come to the Mission to live. He had prayed for him often in the quiet church. But his prayers had not been answered.

"Pray without ceasing," the understanding padre said when Francisco took his problem to him again.

Busy days at the Mission kept the boy from journeying to the mountains again. He helped gather the late harvest of grapes, apples, and olives. The palominos needed new stalls in their adobe shelter to protect the newborn colts from winter rains.

Francisco spent many hours in the new corral training Monte to trot, canter, or gallop at signal. On his birthday the boy would ride the horse in his first race against the best horsemen from neighboring ranchos.

December 21, 1812, was an unpromising day. Heavy clouds hung across the mountains, shutting them from view. The air was oppressive. Horses moved restlessly about in their stalls.

While currying Monte, Francisco noticed his unusual restlessness. The horse twitched at every unexpected sound. He seemed to be listening nervously. Even Francisco's gentle hand could not quite soothe and reassure him.

When the race was begun, Francisco did not need to urge Monte to do his best. The horse and rider sped down the road, almost abreast of the swiftest horses of the neighboring ranchos. At the final stretch Francisco leaned far forward and whispered eagerly, "Come, Monte! Come on!"

The crowd cheered when the creamy palomino

gained on the others and at last won the race. Francisco was excited and pleased, but Monte reared and bucked alarmingly. Perhaps the noise and confusion were disturbing him.

The boy dismounted and led the horse away from the crowd to the quiet of the adobe shelter. But Monte trembled there, too, even while Francisco was talking to him.

"Good Monte," he whispered. "There was never another horse like you." He stroked the sleek coat a few moments and tried to calm the horse. "I'll be back again in a minute to give you a rubdown, Monte," he promised. "You see, the padre is waiting to make a speech. He is going to tell everyone that you are mine and that today on my birthday I am to become the trainer of all palominos."

The horse shook his head and pawed at the adobe floor. Reluctantly Francisco left him and hurried out to join the crowd. As the boy climbed to the platform Father Payéras was beginning to speak in his low, musical voice.

In the distance there was a rumbling, growling sound. Francisco glanced up at the threatening black clouds. Could it be a thunderstorm? The rumbling continued. It grew louder and louder. The platform swayed beneath their feet. The earth

shook and trembled. Adobe walls tottered and crashed to the ground.

Francisco and the padre jumped down from the platform. For a moment all the Indians stood paralyzed with terror at seeing the church, their homes, and all the Mission crashing about them.

"Los temblores! Los temblores!" they screamed in panic. Then they turned away from the Mission. They pushed and crowded one another on their way toward the hills. "Chupu angry! Chupu angry!" They chanted their old tribal refrain in low tones that gradually rose to a high pitch.

"Wait! Wait!" shouted the padre. But no one waited to hear his plea. Francisco had left immediately too—but not to go to the hills. Straight across the plaza he sped. He avoided the corridors where huge sections of fallen walls already blocked the way. At every step the earth shook. Roofs cracked open and dropped their red tiles in his path.

As he passed the ruins of the church, the bells began to clang, rocked by an invisible hand. They clanged and tolled their ominous warning until at last they were overthrown and came hurtling down from their wall with one final alarm before they were half-buried in the ground.

Dodging falling rocks and stones, the boy at last

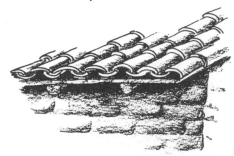

reached the adobe shelter. But the door was now jammed shut. Here, too, walls were shaking. Some of the walls had already tumbled down. Quickly Francisco leaped over a broken archway, then ran down the corridor between the stalls.

In the last one his horse was pulling and jerking at its halter, stamping and kicking against bars. "Monte! Monte!" Francisco cried. At his touch the horse grew quieter and allowed the boy to lead him out of the ruins which still echoed with the crash of heavy timbers and thick adobe walls.

Outside, the clouds had loosed their floodgates. Yet above the sound of the downpour were heard new thunders of the angry earth. With a sudden, violent wrench, the mountain back of the Mission cracked wide open. Torrents of black sand and water gushed out and poured down the canyon.

Francisco and Monte started across the plaza, almost blinded by the furious downpour that had turned morning light into semidarkness. In the boy's haste to find the padre he collided with another scurrying figure.

"My son! My grandson!" Chief Neuia threw his arms around the boy. Pent-up words tumbled from his lips. "I missed you! I saw Mission Indians fleeing—on trail. They told me of Mission ruins.

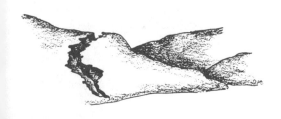

Come! Come home before it is too late. We belong together. We must never be separated. Chupu angry!"

Until Francisco had thought of his horse, he had been as terrified as any of the other Indians. And now as the earth shook with fresh violence, he was again afraid. But the ruined Mission was not entirely forsaken. A short distance away he saw Father Payéras running toward him, carrying one of the broken statues from the church. On the other side of Francisco stood his grandfather, who had just said they must never be separated. Now was the time to show his faith in the Mission God! Now was the time to stand firm.

Francisco had to shout to his grandfather above the roar of the torrents. "Chupu may be angry! But the Mission God has saved the good padre and me!"

Even in the downpour he could see the expression of amazement cross his grandfather's wrinkled face. "Stay! Stay here with us," the boy pleaded. "We can rebuild all that was destroyed! We can show other Indians that the anger of Chupu is far less powerful than the love of the Mission God."

The padre's lips moved in silent prayer. Then the boy and the padre listened while Chief Neuia decided: "I stay with Mission God."

The Wishing Chair *(Mission San Miguel)*

The legend of the Wishing Chair and what happened to a Tulare Indian girl who sat in it.

The Bear Hunter *(Mission San Antonio)*

An exciting account of the bear hunt that saved the Mission from starvation.

Volume 5

Clemente's Christmas *(Mission Soledad)*

A tale of Christmas, showing how a lonely sheepherder found friends through the Nativity play.

Juan of Carmel *(Mission San Carlos)*

An Indian boy's adventure in early days of Carmel Mission.

The Magic Barrel Organ *(Mission San Juan Bautista)*

The young Indian singer who lost his voice, but found it in time to stop the enemy.

Volume 6

Miguel and the Pirates *(Mission Santa Cruz)*

A Mission Indian boy's experience with pirates.

Little Lost Girl *(Mission Santa Clara)*

The story of a captive Indian girl who found happiness in her new Mission home.

The Music-Maker *(Mission San José)*

The story of an Indian boy who loved music.

Volume 7

Chamis and Lilote *(Mission San Francisco de Asís)*

The romantic story of the first Indians at Mission Dolores.

The Warrior of San Rafael *(Mission San Rafael)*

A lame Indian boy's victory over a dreaded kidnapper.

Big Chief Solano *(Mission San Francisco Solano)*

The story of a powerful Indian chief and his decision for peace with the white man.